STORY STUDIO

People express themselves through stories and pictures.

SCHOLASTIC
LITERACY
PLACE®

Copyright acknowledgments and credits appear on page 144, which constitutes an extension of this copyright page.

Visit an
Author's Studio

People express
themselves through
stories and pictures.

Stories Often Told

Stories are told again and again.

Author! Author!

Authors write many kinds of stories.

Tell a Story

We create our own stories and pictures.

Detail from Henri Matisse, *Piano Lesson*

Trade Books

The following books accompany this *Story Studio* SourceBook.

Fantasy
Dear Peter Rabbit
by Alma Flor Ada
illustrated by Leslie Tryon

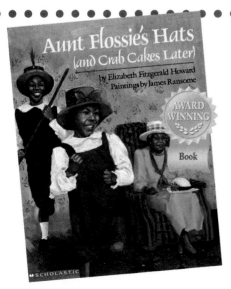

Realistic Fiction
The Stories Julian Tells
by Ann Cameron
illustrated by Ann Strugnell

Humorous Fiction
The True Story of the 3 Little Pigs!
by Jon Scieszka
illustrated by Lane Smith

Big Book

Realistic Fiction
Aunt Flossie's Hats (and Crab Cakes Later)
by Elizabeth Fitzgerald Howard
illustrated by James Ransome

Stories Often Told

Stories are told again and again.

See how one artist's pictures changed a scary story to a funny one! Then discover some favorite stories told in different ways.

Meet a new and different Goldilocks. Then laugh as three actors make the three bears say all the wrong things.

9

RED RIDING HOOD

Retold and Illustrated by

JAMES MARSHALL

A long time ago
in a simple cottage
beside the deep, dark woods,
there lived a pretty child
called Red Riding Hood.
She was kind and considerate,
and everybody loved her.

One afternoon
Red Riding Hood's mother called to her.
"Granny isn't feeling up to snuff today,"
she said, "so I've baked
her favorite custard
as a little surprise.
Be a good girl and
take it to her, will you?"
Red Riding Hood was delighted.
She loved going to Granny's—
even though it meant crossing
the deep, dark woods.

When the custard
had cooled, Red Riding Hood's
mother wrapped it up
and put it in a basket.
"Now, whatever you do,"
she said,
"go straight to Granny's,
do not tarry,
do not speak
to any strangers."
"Yes, Mama,"
said Red Riding Hood.

15

Before long she was
in the deepest part of the woods.
"Oooh," she said. "This is scary."

Suddenly a large wolf appeared.
"Good afternoon, my dear,"
he said.
"Care to stop for a little chat?"
"Oh, gracious me,"
said Red Riding Hood.
"Mama said not to speak
to any strangers."

But the wolf had *such*
charming manners.
"And where are you going,
sweet thing?" he said.
"I'm on my way to visit Granny,
who lives in the pretty yellow house
on the other side of the woods,"
said Red Riding Hood.
"She's feeling poorly,
and I'm taking her a surprise."
"You don't say," said the wolf.
Just then he had a delightful idea.
No reason why I can't eat them *both*,
he thought.
"Allow me to escort you," he said.
"You never know what might be
lurking about."
"You're too kind," said Red Riding Hood.

Beyond the forest they came
to a patch of sunflowers.
"Why not pick a few?"
suggested the wolf.
"Grannies *love* flowers,
you know."
But while Red Riding Hood was
picking a pretty bouquet,
the clever wolf hurried on ahead
to Granny's house.

"Who is it?"
called out Granny.
"It is I, your delicious—er—
darling granddaughter,"
said the wolf
in a high voice.
"The door is unlocked,"
said Granny.

"Surprise!"
cried the wolf.
Granny was furious at
having her reading interrupted.
"Get out of here,
you horrid thing!"
she cried.

But the wolf gobbled her right up.
He didn't even bother to chew.
"Tasty," he said, patting his belly,
"so tasty."
Just then he heard footsteps
on the garden path.
"Here comes dessert!"
And losing no time, he put on
Granny's cap and glasses,
jumped into bed, and pulled up the covers.

"Who is it?"
he called out
in his sweetest granny voice.
"It is I, your little granddaughter,"
said Red Riding Hood.
"The door is unlocked,"
said the wolf.

Red Riding Hood was distressed
at seeing her grandmother so changed.
"Why, Granny," she said,
"what big eyes you have."
"The better to see you, my dear," said the wolf.
"And Granny, what long arms you have."
"The better to hug you, my dear," said the wolf.
"And Granny, what big teeth you have."

"THE BETTER TO EAT YOU, MY DEAR!"
cried the wolf.

And he gobbled her right up.
"I'm so wicked," he said. "*So* wicked."
But really he was
enormously pleased with himself.
And having enjoyed such a
heavy meal, he was soon snoring away.
A hunter passing by was alarmed
by the frightful racket.
"That doesn't sound like Granny!"
he said.

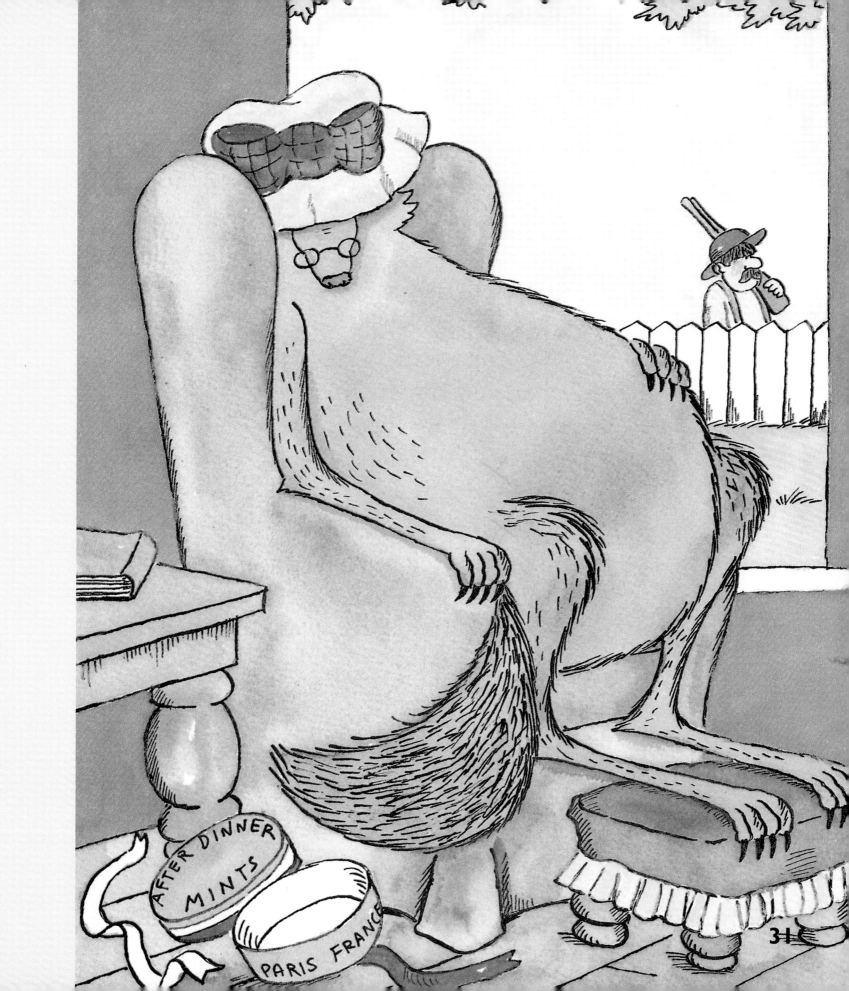

And so the brave hunter
jumped in the window,
killed the sleeping wolf,
and cut him open.
Out jumped Granny and Red Riding Hood.
"We're ever so grateful,"
said Red Riding Hood.
"That wicked wolf won't trouble
you again," said the hunter.
"It was so dark in there I couldn't read a *word*,"
said Granny.
Red Riding Hood promised never,
ever to speak to another stranger,
charming manners or not.

And she never did.

And Still More Tales

People have been telling tales like *Little Red Riding Hood* for hundreds of years. Sometimes they change the words or pictures to make the tale even more interesting or funny. Sometimes the setting is changed to show how different people live. A big bad wolf might become a city cat or a fox! Cinderella can even be a boy!

Here are some different tellings of favorite tales.

LITTLE RED RIDING HOOD

A Rhyming Tale

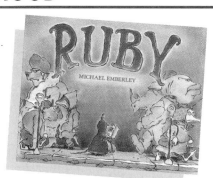

A City Tale

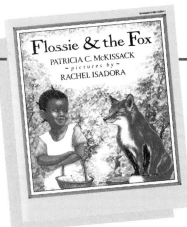

A Southern Tale

THE FROG PRINCE

A Beautiful Tale

A Funny Tale

The Happily Ever After Tale

CINDERELLA

The Stepsister's Tale

A Sports Tale

A Chinese Tale

JACK AND THE BEANSTALK

The Classic Tale

An Old-Fashioned Tale

The Tale Continues

THE MOUSE BRIDE

A Mayan Tale

A Japanese Tale

A Chinese Tale

35

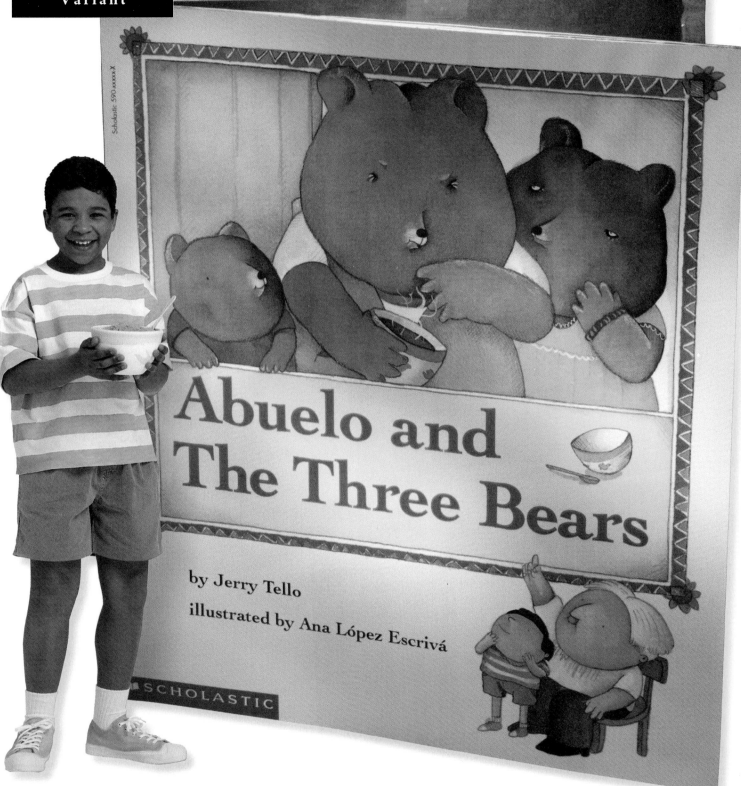

Abuelo and The Three Bears

by Jerry Tello

illustrated by Ana López Escrivá

SCHOLASTIC

It was a quiet Sunday. Emilio and his grandfather sat on the front porch.

"Abuelo," said Emilio, "do we have to wait much longer? When will everybody get here?"

"Your cousins will arrive soon," Abuelo answered, "and we'll have a fine dinner. I'll tell you a story to help pass the time."

Once there were three bears who lived in the woods—Papá Bear, Mamá Bear, and their little Osito. One Sunday morning, Papá Bear woke up as grumpy as ever. Then he smelled something good. "Mmmm, frijoles!" he said.

"Abuelo, you're joking!" laughed Emilio. "Bears don't like beans!"

"Well, all the bears I know like frijoles," said Abuelo.

38

Papá Bear got up and rushed down to the kitchen.
"Buenos días," said Papá Bear to Mamá Bear and Osito.

Papá Bear sat down at the table and tucked a napkin under his chin. "How are the frijoles? Are they ready yet?" he asked. "Yes," answered Mamá Bear, "but they're still too hot to eat."

"I can't wait," said Papá Bear. "I'm so hungry I could eat an elephant."

"Abuelo," said Emilio, "bears don't eat elephants."

"Emilio," answered Abuelo, "you must never argue with a hungry bear."

Stubborn Papá Bear didn't listen to Mamá Bear's warning.

"¡Ay!" he growled, jumping out of his chair. "These beans are too hot!"

"I told you so," said Mamá Bear. "Why don't we take a walk into town while they cool?"

"All right," grumbled Papá Bear, whose mouth was still burning. So the bears left their breakfast to cool and went out.

Just then, in another part of the woods, a girl named Trencitas set out from her house to visit her friend, Osito. She was called Trencitas because she had long black braids.

"Abuelo," Emilio called out, "the girl in this story is called Goldilocks and she has blond hair."

"Goldilocks?" Abuelo shrugged. "In my story it was Trencitas with her long black braids who came to visit. And she was hungry, too!"

When Trencitas arrived at Osito's house, she noticed that the door was open. So she stepped inside and followed her nose until she came to the three bowls of beans.

First Trencitas tasted some beans from the great big bowl, but they were too hot. Then she tasted some from the medium-sized bowl, but they were too cold. Finally she tasted some from the little bowl, and they were just right. So she finished them all up.

Now Trencitas decided to sit in the living room and wait for the bears to return. She sat in the great big chair, but it was too hard. She sat in the medium-sized chair, but it was too soft. Then she sat in the little chair, and it was just right until... CRASH!

43

"Abuelo, what's Trencitas going to do?" asked Emilio. "She broke her friend's chair."

"Don't worry," Abuelo said. "She'll come back later with glue and leave it like new."

Trencitas was feeling very sleepy. She went upstairs to take a rest. First she tried the great big bed, but the blanket was scratchy. Then she tried the medium-sized bed, but it was too lumpy. Finally she tried the little bed. It was too small, but it was so cozy and soft that Trencitas soon fell asleep.

When the three bears came home, Papá Bear headed straight to the kitchen to eat his frijoles.

"¡Ay!" he growled when he saw his bowl. "Somebody's been eating my beans."

"And somebody's been eating my beans," said Mamá Bear.

"And there's only one bean left in my bowl," said Osito.

Then the three bears went into the living room.

"¡Ay!" said Papá Bear, when he saw that his chair had been moved. "Somebody's been sitting in my chair."

"And somebody's been sitting in my chair," said Mamá Bear.

"And my chair is all over the place!" said Osito.

The three bears climbed the stairs to check out the bedrooms. Papá Bear went first. Mamá Bear and Osito followed behind him.

"¡Ay!" said Papá Bear, when he looked in the bedroom. "Somebody's been sleeping in my bed."

"And somebody's been sleeping in my bed," said Mamá Bear.

"Look who's sleeping in my bed!" said Osito. He ran over to Trencitas and woke her up. Then they all had a good laugh.

By now it was getting late. Mamá Bear said they'd walk Trencitas home to make sure she got there safely.

Papá Bear did not like this idea. "Another walk!" he growled. "What about my frijoles?"

"There'll be beans at my house," offered Trencitas.

"I'll bet that made Papá Bear happy," said Emilio.

"You're right," said Abuelo. "Here's what happened next...."

47

When they all arrived at Trencitas's house, they sat down at a long table with Trencitas's parents, grandparents, uncles, aunts, and lots of cousins. They ate pork and fish and chicken and tortillas and beans and salsa so hot it brought tears to their eyes. And they laughed and shared stories.

"So you see, Emilio," said Abuelo, "Papá Bear had to wait a long time to eat his frijoles. But, in the end, he had a wonderful meal and lots of fun, just as you will when your cousins arrive."

"Is that the end of the story?"
Emilio asked.

"Yes," answered Abuelo, "and
it's the end of your waiting, too!"

GLOSSARY	
Abuelo	Grandfather
Osito	Little Bear
Frijoles	Beans
Buenos días	Good morning
¡Ay!	Oh!
Trencitas	Little Braids
Tortillas	Thin corn pancakes
Salsa	Spicy tomato and chile dip

from BIG BEAR'S TREASURY

SOURCE

BIG BEAR'S TREASURY
A Children's Anthology

Poetry
Collection

WHO'S BEEN SLEEPING IN MY PORRIDGE?

by Colin McNaughton

"Who's been sitting in my bed?"
    said the mama bear crossly.
"Who's been eating my chair?"
    said the baby bear weepily.
"Who's been sleeping in my porridge?"
    said the papa bear angrily.
"Wait a minute," said Goldilocks.

"Why can't you guys just stick
    to the script? Now let's try it
again and this time, no messing around."

Author! Author!

Authors write many kinds of stories.

Watch a pet dinosaur become an important part of a family.

Find out why the author of the dinosaur story loves to write about make-believe things.

Join a girl as she discovers treasure in her backyard. Then find out why the author of this story wrote about this girl.

Little Grunt
and the
Big Egg

A Prehistoric Fairy Tale

Tomie
dePaola

AWARD
WINNING

Author/
Illustrator

Once upon a time, in a big cave, past the volcano on the left, lived the Grunt Tribe. There was Unca Grunt, Ant Grunt, Granny Grunt, Mama Grunt, and Papa Grunt. Their leader was Chief Rockhead Grunt. The smallest Grunt of all was Little Grunt.

One Saturday morning, Mama Grunt said to Little Grunt, "Little Grunt, tomorrow the Ugga-Wugga Tribe is coming for Sunday brunch. Could you please go outside and gather two dozen eggs?"

"Yes, Mama Grunt," said Little Grunt, and off he went.

At that time of year, eggs were hard to find. Little Grunt looked and looked. No luck. He was getting tired.

"What am I going to do?" he said to himself. "I can't find a single egg. I'll try one more place."

And it was a good thing that he did, because there, in the one more place, was the biggest egg Little Grunt had ever seen.

It was too big to carry. It was too far to roll. And besides, Little Grunt had to be very careful. Eggs break *very* easily.

Little Grunt thought and thought.

"I know," he said. He gathered some of the thick pointy leaves that were growing nearby. He wove them into a mat. Then he carefully rolled the egg on top of it. He pulled and pulled and pulled the egg all the way home.

"My goodness," said the Grunt Tribe. "Ooga, ooga, what an egg! That will feed us *and* the Ugga-Wuggas. And even the Grizzler Tribe. Maybe we should invite *them* to Sunday brunch, too."

"I'll be able to make that special omelet I've been wanting to," said Mama Grunt.

"Ooga, ooga! Yummy! Yummy!" said all the Grunts.

They put the egg near the hearth, and then they all
went to bed.

That night, by the flickering firelight, the egg began
to make noise. CLICK, CRACK went the egg. CLICK,
CRACK, CLUNK. A big piece fell to the floor. CLICK,
CRACK, CLUNK, PLOP. The egg broke in half, and
instead of the big egg sitting by the fire . . .

There was a baby dinosaur!

"Waaangh," cried the baby dinosaur. And all the Grunt Tribe woke up.

"Ooga, ooga!" they said. "What are we going to do?"

"There goes the brunch!" said Unca Grunt.

"What will the Ugga-Wuggas say?" said Ant Grunt.

"I bet I'm allergic to that thing," said Papa Grunt.

Chief Rockhead Grunt said, "All I know is it can't stay . . ."

But before he could finish, Little Grunt said, "May I keep him? Please? *Please*?"

"Every boy needs a pet," said Granny Grunt.

Some of the Grunts said yes. Some of the Grunts said no. But it was finally decided that Little Grunt could keep the baby dinosaur.

"Against my better judgment," mumbled Chief Rockhead Grunt.

"Oh, well, I suppose I can make pancakes for Sunday brunch," said Mama Grunt.

"I'm going to call him George," said Little Grunt.

Little Grunt and George became great pals.

But there was a problem. The cave stayed the same size, but George didn't. He began to grow.

And GROW. And GROW.

The cave got very crowded.

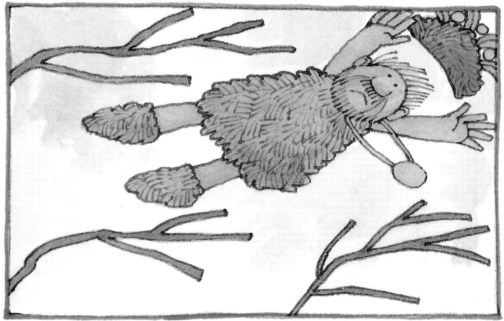

And there were other problems.

George wasn't housebroken.

George ate ALL the leaves off ALL the trees and ALL
the bushes ALL around the cave. But still he was hungry.

George liked to play—rough. George stepped
on things.

And when he sneezed—well, it was a disaster.

"Ooga, ooga! Enough is enough!" said the Grunts.

"Either that dinosaur goes, or I go," said Unca Grunt.

"I spend all day getting food for him," said Ant Grunt.

"Achoo!" said Papa Grunt. "I told you I was allergic to him."

"He stepped on all my cooking pots and broke them," said Mama Grunt.

"I guess it wasn't a good idea to keep him," said
Granny Grunt. "How about a nice *little* cockroach.
They make nice pets."

"I'm in charge here," said Chief Rockhead Grunt.
"And I say, *That giant lizard goes!*"

"Ooga, ooga! Yes! Yes!" said all the Grunts.

"But you promised," said Little Grunt.

The next morning, Little Grunt took George away
from the cave, out to where he had found him in the
first place.

"Good-bye, George," said Little Grunt. "I'll sure
miss you."

"Waaargh," said George.

Big tears rolled down both their cheeks. Sadly,
Little Grunt watched as George walked slowly into
the swamp.

"I'll never see him again," sobbed Little Grunt.

The days and months went by, and Little Grunt still missed George. He dreamed about him at night and drew pictures of him by day.

"Little Grunt certainly misses that dinosaur," said Mama Grunt.

"He'll get over it," said Papa Grunt.

"It's nice and peaceful here again," said Ant and Unca Grunt.

"I still say a cockroach makes a nice pet," said Granny Grunt.

"Ooga, ooga. Torches out. Everyone in bed," said Chief Rockhead.

That night, the cave started to shake. The floor
began to pitch, and loud rumblings filled the air.

"Earthquake!" cried the Grunts, and they rushed
to the opening of the cave.

"No, it's not," said Granny Grunt. "Look! Volcano!"

And sure enough, the big volcano was erupting all over the place. Steam and rocks and black smoke shot out of the top. Around the cave, big rocks and boulders tumbled and bounced.

"We're trapped! We're trapped!" shouted the
Grunts. "What are we going to do?"

"Don't ask me!" said Chief Rockhead. "I resign."

"Now we have no leader," cried Ant Grunt.

"Now we're really in trouble!" shouted Papa Grunt.
The lava was pouring out of the volcano in a wide,
flaming river and was heading straight for the cave.

There wasn't enough time for the Grunts to escape.
All of a sudden, the Grunts heard a different noise.
"Waaargh! Wonk!"

"It's George," cried Little Grunt. "He's come to save us."

"Ooga, ooga! Quick!" said the Grunts as they all jumped
on George's long neck and long back and long tail.

And before you could say Tyrannosaurus rex,
George carried them far away to safety.

"As your new leader," Papa Grunt said, "I say this is our new cave!"

"I like the kitchen," said Mama Grunt.

"Now, when I was the leader . . ." said Plain Rockhead Grunt.

"When do we eat?" said Unca Grunt.

"I can't wait to start decorating," said Ant Grunt.

"I always say a change of scenery keeps you from getting old," said Granny Grunt.

"And George can live right next door," said
Little Grunt.

"Where is George?" asked Mama Grunt. "I haven't
seen him all afternoon."

"Ooga, ooga. Here, George," called the Grunts.

"Waaargh," answered George.

"Look!" said Little Grunt.

"Oh no!" said the Grunts.

There was George, sitting on a pile of big eggs.

"I guess I'd better call George Georgina!"
said Little Grunt.
And they all lived happily ever after.

Tomie dePaola

Author and Artist

An author can make ANYTHING happen in a story. And so can YOU!

Do you like to draw pictures? When Tomie dePaola was a little boy, he loved drawing so much that he decided to become an artist. He dreamed of telling stories someday with his art.

Now dePaola is famous for his art and storytelling. His childhood dream has come true. He says he always knew it would.

Tomie dePaola

Author and Artist

Here's how author and artist Tomie dePaola puts stories together in his studio.

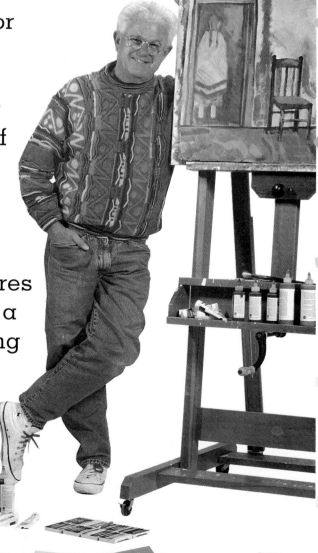

Tomie dePaola gets ideas for his books from everywhere. Sometimes the ideas come from his childhood. At other times, they come right out of his imagination.

Perhaps because drawing was his first love, he gets some story ideas from pictures he draws. Strega Nona was a character he started doodling one day, just for fun. He decided that she was just right for a story about a woman with a special pasta pot.

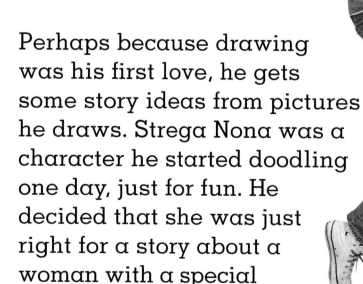

Even if a story idea comes from a drawing, Mr. dePaola doesn't do the pictures first. He works out the story first because he thinks that the story is more important. The pictures add to the story.

Tomie dePaola tries to create stories and art that mean a lot to children. He wants to be part of their lives. He says, "I share my feelings with children, and I think they appreciate that."

Tomie dePaola's
Tips to Young Authors and Artists

1 Decide who to write about. Will your characters be people or animals?

2 Decide what you want your characters to do. Will it be real or make-believe? Will it be funny, sad, or scary?

3 As you write your story, draw pictures that tell the story as much as the words do.

The Treasure Hunt

by Angela Shelf Medearis

illustrated by Larry Johnson

AWARD
WINNING

Author

SCHOLASTIC

Marcy pushed open the door to her big sister's room. She could see Annie sitting at her desk, bent over a notebook. Annie's pen was moving quickly across the page.

Marcy sat on her sister's bed and watched Annie
write. Marcy began to hum a little song.

Annie put down her pen. She looked at Marcy.
Marcy smiled and stopped humming.

"Will you play a game with me?" Marcy asked
sweetly. "You can go first."

"Just one game," Annie warned. "Then you
are going to leave, and I am going to finish writing
my story."

Marcy pulled her favorite game down from the shelf. Together, the two girls opened the game board and set up the pieces. They took turns moving their markers around the board. The game did not last very long. Annie won.

"You cheated," Marcy said to her sister.

"I did not!" Annie groaned. "You say that every time we play! Now go on. I want to finish writing my story."

Annie went back to her desk. She opened the notebook and started to write.

Marcy peeked over her sister's shoulder. "What's your story about?" she asked.

"I'm writing about a secret treasure," Annie explained. "The girl in the story solves a mystery and finds lots of gold buried under a tree."

"That sounds like a good story," said Marcy. "Can I read it?"

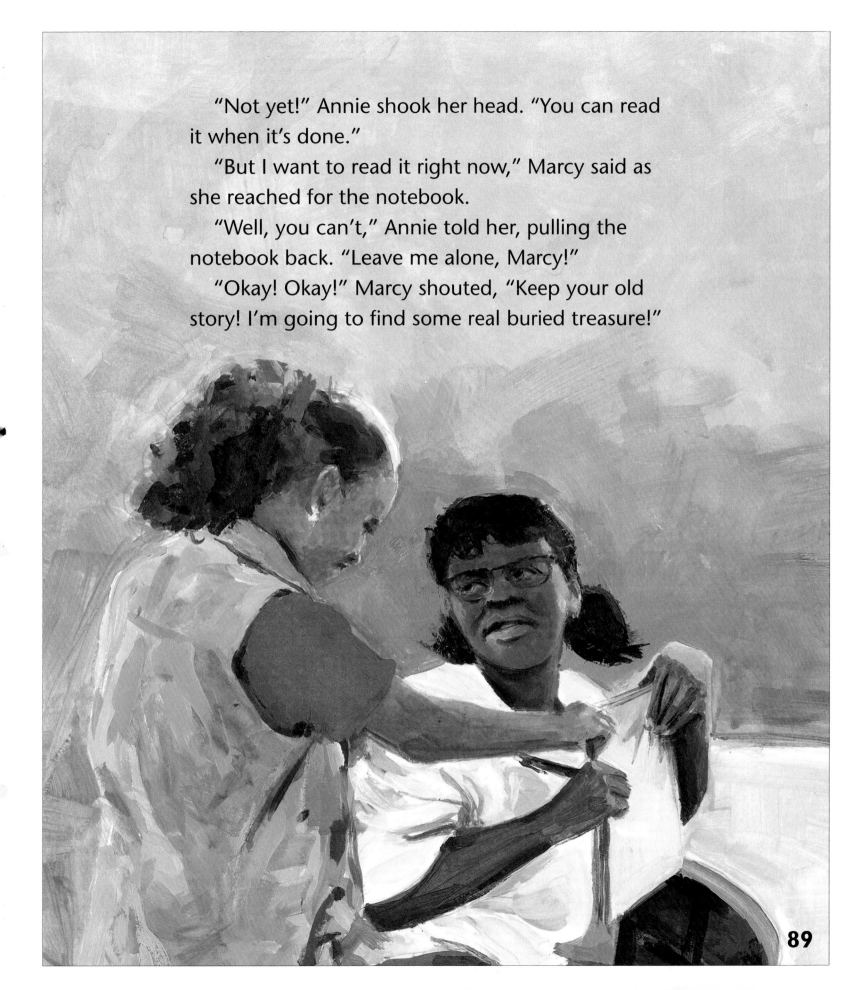

"Not yet!" Annie shook her head. "You can read it when it's done."

"But I want to read it right now," Marcy said as she reached for the notebook.

"Well, you can't," Annie told her, pulling the notebook back. "Leave me alone, Marcy!"

"Okay! Okay!" Marcy shouted, "Keep your old story! I'm going to find some real buried treasure!"

Marcy ran outside and into the backyard. She climbed onto a swing and kicked her feet hard. The swing carried her high in the air. She could see over the fence and down the hill. In the distance Marcy could see the lake in the park, where some people were fishing.

Biscuit, Marcy's dog, came out into the yard. Marcy stopped swinging and patted Biscuit on the head. The dog wagged his tail. Then he curled up to take a nap under a tree.

Suddenly, Marcy had an idea. She got a shovel and a jar and started to dig right next to where Biscuit was trying to sleep.

"Wake up, Biscuit!" Marcy said. "I'll bet there's a treasure buried underneath this tree. Let's see if we can find it!"

Marcy and Biscuit dug for a long time. Soon there was a small mound of dirt near the tree. Marcy's shovel hit something hard.

"A treasure!" Marcy yelled, and she dug deeper and deeper. At last she could see what it was.

"Oh," Marcy said sadly. "It's only a bone."

Biscuit was not disappointed. He took the bone, lay down, and chewed happily.

Marcy started digging again. Her shovel scooped up damp, dark dirt. Worms wiggled out of the dirt. The worms were getting in Marcy's way.

Marcy looked over the fence and down at the lake and sighed. "I found an old bone for you," she told Biscuit. "And I found lots of wiggly worms. What kind of a treasure is that?"

Then Marcy had a new idea. She got more jars from the garage and started to fill them with worms. She found a big box and carefully put the jars full of worms into the box.

Annie called from the window, "I'm finished with my story, Marcy. You can read it now."

"Sorry, Annie! Now I'm busy." Marcy answered. "I'll read it later."

Marcy found some paper and a pen and made a big sign. She carried the box and sign around to the front porch.

Soon some neighbors came by and read her sign.

"This is just what I need," said Mr. Stevenson from next door. "I'll take two jars." He took out two dollar bills and gave them to Marcy.

"The whole family is going fishing this afternoon," said Mrs. Martínez from down the street. "I'll take five jars." She handed Marcy a crisp five-dollar bill.

Marcy sold every jar in the box.

After she took down her sign and cleaned up, Marcy went into the kitchen to count her money.

When Annie came into the kitchen for a snack, she saw Marcy sitting at the table.

"Where did you get all that money?" asked Annie.

"Oh," said Marcy, "I found some treasure buried in the backyard."

"But there is no treasure in the backyard," Annie said. "That only happens in stories."

"That's not true," Marcy told her sister. "You can find a treasure if you know where to dig!"

My Story: Angela

Angela Shelf Medearis is an author who remembers what it's like to be a kid. She says:

Many of my best story ideas come from things that happened to me when I was little.

Shelf Medearis

Ms. Medearis's father used to tell her stories about long ago when their people were kings and queens in Africa. In Medearis's book called *Our People*, a little girl has a father who tells her wonderful stories about real African and African-American heroes.

When Ms. Medearis was little, her mother called her Annie. In two of her books, a character named Annie does things based on what really happened to the author. In *Annie's Gifts*, Annie tries and tries to find an instrument she can play. *The Treasure Hunt* tells what happens when Annie's little sister Marcy wants to play and Annie does not.

Like the Annie in her stories, the author started writing when she was very young. "Any child who writes is a writer," says Ms. Medearis. "Writing is something you can do at any age—I love that about writing! Anybody can do it, and every one of us has something interesting to say!"

Tell a Story

We create our own stories and pictures.

Find out if Jacob ever gets an idea for a story.

Learn the steps in making a story into a published book.

Use your imagination to look for stories told in paintings.

Detail from Henri Matisse, *Piano Lesson*

Meet an amazing girl who started painting stories at the age of three.

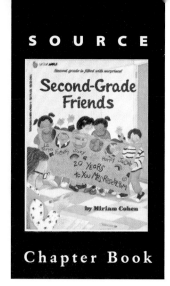

SOURCE

Chapter Book

The Real Author

By Miriam Cohen

Illustrated by Diane Palmisciano

A Real Author was coming to talk to second grade about how to be a writer and have imagination. Mrs. Rosebloom was going to put up their work in the hall so the Real Author could see what good writers they were.

Everybody was writing and writing, except Jacob. He put his head down on his desk, and started worrying. "In second grade you have to be much smarter than in first grade. You have to work, work, work, every minute. I can't do all this hard work! In first grade I was happy all the time."

Franky was busy with something under his desk. He grinned at Jacob. He was folding a piece of paper so it would make a firecracker noise when he pulled it open. Franky never worried.

Gregory was writing a funny story. He stopped and poked Jacob. "Are you thinking again?" Gregory admired Jacob a lot. He was Jacob's real friend. "Why don't you start writing, Jacob? The Author is almost here," said Gregory.

Jacob touched Suzy on her back just a teeny bit with his pencil eraser. She turned around and stared at him through her new glasses. "Stop that!"

Jacob leaned over and whispered, "Hey, Nathan, you want to hear a good riddle?"

Nathan looked annoyed. "Jacob, I'm trying to work."

"I don't know why the kids don't like me as much as they used to," Jacob said to himself. "Probably they won't even come to my birthday party." Then he said to Franky, "I wish I was still in the first grade."

"You're crazy!" said Franky.

The twins LaToya and LaTanya stopped writing. "The Real Author is coming, Jacob," said LaToya.

"We're going to get his autograph," said LaTanya.

"You'd better hurry, Jacob," they both said. Then they put their heads down over their papers again.

Jacob liked the yellow plastic airplanes, blue teddy bears, and red hearts holding all their little pigtails. He was counting them when he saw Suzy looking at him through her glasses. They made her eyes look very big and smart.

She shook her head. "Jacob, you're not working. It's very important for a Real Author to meet you."

"Oh, yes," said Katy. "I just love a Real Author. Once my aunt was shopping, and she saw a Real Author, and she ran after him to get his autograph. But it was somebody else who wasn't even an author."

Jacob said, "I would like to write a book. But it would take too long. Besides, I might get the writer's cramp." Mrs. Rosebloom had told them how writers' hands could pinch up from too much writing.

"Yeah, or a headache," Gregory said. "Nathan's going to have a *big* headache. Look how much he wrote!" Nathan's story already went down two pages and halfway on another.

Jacob covered up his empty paper with his hand.

Mrs. Rosebloom told him, "Why don't you try a poem?" So Jacob decided to write one. Poems could be really short. He looked up at the ceiling. He drew pencil lines between the corduroy on his pants. Finally he thought of a poem:

"I like my teacher.
She is nice
Because she isn't . . ."

It was really hard to think of what would rhyme with "nice." Then he thought of it —"pice."
"What is 'pice'?" LaToya and LaTanya asked.
"I don't know, but it rhymes," Jacob said.

Some of the kids laughed, because "pice" sounded so funny.

"The Real Author is coming to see your work in a few minutes," Mrs. Rosebloom told the class.

When Jacob heard Mrs. Rosebloom say that, he quickly chewed his poem into little pieces. Then he dropped them in the gerbils' cage. It was all right because gerbils have torn-up paper in the bottom of their cages anyway.

Honey was ready to read her story to the class. She was the biggest and roundest and strongest kid in second grade. She was also the nicest. Honey liked everyone. She always gave anybody who wanted one an extra-big cookie from her lunch.

"Class, let's all be ready to help Honey with her story," said Mrs. Rosebloom. "Remember, give your opinions in a kind way."

Honey began, "Once there was a cute little girl named Lou-Ann." (That was Honey's real name.) "She was the strongest in her whole class. But her stepmother said, 'There is a dance-ball, and you cannot go to it!' So she was crying in the kitchen. Then a fairy jumped out of the microwave and said, 'Come with me, and you will win a prize.' "

Suzy whispered very loud to Katy, "She's just copying Cinderella."

The teacher said, "Lots of fairy tales use those ideas, Suzy. And writers always put some of themselves in their stories." Then she sat down next to Honey. "Maybe you could try something that is not *quite* so much like Cinderella."

Mrs. Rosebloom turned around. "Have you written anything yet, Jacob?"

Jacob shook his head. He looked worried.

Katy told Jacob, "Once I didn't have any imagination, and I closed my eyes, and I got some."

Jacob closed his eyes.

"What do you see?" everybody wanted to know.

"I see . . . beavers," Jacob said. Once he and his dad watched a TV special about beavers, and Jacob got very interested in them. Every week he took out the same beaver book at library period.

"Beavers are boring." Franky laughed. "Jacob, you're *weird*!"

"Why don't you write about 'My Fishing Trip with My Father'?" said LaToya.

"I never went on a fishing trip with my father." Jacob would have loved to go fishing, but his father wasn't really that kind of a father.

"Well, what *do* you do with your father?" LaTanya asked.

"Sometimes we read together on the sofa. He reads his newspaper, and I read my library book."

"Well, what happens then?"

"We just read, and breathe," said Jacob.

"You should get your father to play some baseball with you," said LaTanya.

"Like ours does," said LaToya.

Jacob didn't want to mention it, but his father didn't know how to play baseball.

Honey was getting bored working on her story. She smiled at Jacob. In kindergarten, Honey used to put Jacob in the doll-buggy. "I'm the mommy, and you're the baby," she would say. It made Jacob very embarrassed.

Now, she came up behind him. "Hey, look at this! I can pick up Jacob *and* his chair!"

"Put me down!" Jacob shouted.

Mrs. Rosebloom hurried over. "Honey! You could hurt somebody doing that! Put him down this minute!"

Honey went back to her seat and waved at Jacob. Jacob was only mad for a little while. You couldn't stay mad at Honey because she liked you even when you were mad at her.

"My story is ready," Katy said. It was about her Pinky Pony. She really did have a Pinky Pony, just like the one on TV. In the story, Pinky Pony found the rainbow with her little friends, the rabbit, and Raggedy Ann, and "they all had a delicious party."

"I wrote a space science fiction novel," Nathan told the class.

"How many pages does it have?" asked Mrs. Rosebloom.

"Ten, so far," said Nathan.

"Wonderful!" Mrs. Rosebloom said. "But we won't have time to read it out loud now. The Author will be here in just a few minutes. Finish your work quickly, class!"

"But I didn't write anything!" Jacob cried.

"Well, never mind, dear. You can hold the banner we made. It says, 'Welcome Author!' in such colorful letters."

Jacob scuffed his sneaker on the floor. He didn't answer. The teacher patted him, and hurried into the hall to put up their stories.

Jacob was almost crying. "I'm the only one with no imagination—I'll probably grow up without any imagination!"

"Don't make such a fuss," said Suzy. "You can still eat and walk around."

"Don't worry," Honey told him. "You want one of the cupcakes from my lunch?"

Jacob shook his head. "The Author won't even know I'm here! He'll think I can't do anything!"

"We'll tell him," Gregory said. "We'll tell him you can bend your thumb way back and touch your arm. You can show him."

"Why don't you just write about something you're interested in?" LaToya and LaTanya said.

"It's too late! There's no time!" Jacob cried.

Katy ran and got Jacob's pencil and paper. Gregory and Franky sat him down at his desk, and pushed the pencil into his hand. Suddenly Jacob began to write. His ideas kept coming. He almost couldn't write them down fast enough.

"That's the way, Jacob," everybody cheered. "Come on, Jacob!"

The minute Jacob finished, Mrs. Rosebloom put up his story in the hall.

"He's coming!" Everybody ran to peek out the door. The principal was smiling and smiling. She was walking next to the Author and telling him, "Our cafeteria was added in 1985."

"He's supposed to be bigger!" Franky said.

Suzy stared through her new glasses. "He doesn't look right."

Katy said, "He's not supposed to be so old."

Franky said, "Maybe it's not *really* him."

Little kindergarten children, in a line, waved and said, "Hi, Author!"

The Real Author began looking at second grade's stories. "This is so interesting," he said about Nathan's. "What a funny one!" he said about Gregory's. "I like the part about the fairy in the microwave," he said about Honey's story. Then he stopped in front of Jacob's paper. Jacob chewed on his jean jacket collar, he was so nervous.

" 'Why Are There Beavers?' " read the Real Author. He smiled a lot and nodded while he was reading.

"He likes yours!" Gregory whispered to Jacob.

"All of these people have such good imaginations!" the Real Author said.

Gregory poked Jacob. "See, you've got imagination!"

Jacob said, "Well, maybe *sometimes* I do."

"Give yourself a pat on the back for fine work, Jacob," said Mrs. Rosebloom.

And Jacob did.

Did you ever wonder how a story becomes a book? You know that someone has to write the story. But then what happens? Once the story is written, an editor helps the writer change the words to make the story even better.

Here are pages from a book called *Wake Me in Spring*. It is about a bear who is planning to sleep all winter. Look at the changes the editor made. Would you have made these changes?

Wake Me in Spring
pages 4–5

Mouse looked out from his hole, and said, "It's getting cold." He shivered ~~Mouse~~.

Bear scratched his belly and yawned.

"Yes," said Bear. "I feel winter in my bones."

pages 6–7

Bear looked at the calendar ~~and said,~~ "Time for bed!" he said.
" I'm so tired, I will surely sleep all winter long."

"But Bear," Mouse cried, "you'll miss winter!"

The pictures for a book are also done in steps. First an artist makes sketches to see how the pictures should look. Then the artist creates the final pictures that you see in the book.

Look at the sketches that the artist made for pages 4 and 5. Now look at those pages in the book. Do the pictures in the book look like the sketches? What kinds of changes did the artist make?

ARTIST'S SKETCH

Mouse looked out
from his hole and said,
"It's getting cold."
He shivered.

Bear scratched his belly
and yawned.

4

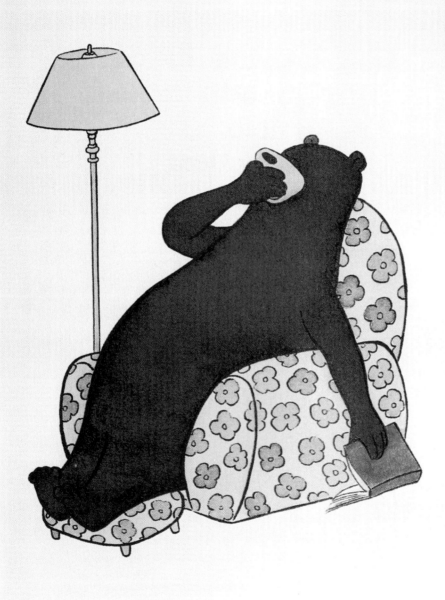

"Yes," said Bear.
"I feel winter in my bones."

5

On pages 6 and 7 of the story, Bear is about to settle down for his long winter sleep. How do Bear and Mouse look in the sketches?

Do you think the changes in the pictures made the story better? Would you have made other kinds of changes?

ARTIST'S SKETCH

Bear looked at the calendar. "Time for bed!" he said. "I'm so tired. I will surely sleep all winter long."

6

"But Bear,"
Mouse cried,
"you'll miss
winter!"

7

The next time you write a story, be your own editor and artist. Remember that to make a story really good, you have to make changes!

from

Stories

by Philip Yenawine

Jacob Lawrence, *The Migration of the Negro*

In pictures, you can make up stories about people . . . and places . . . and things.

Detail from Henri Rousseau, *The Sleeping Gypsy*

Detail from Henri Matisse, *Piano Lesson*

Detail from Pierre Bonnard, *The Breakfast Room*

Detail from Ben Shahn, *Liberation*

**Maybe it's time to eat. What meal is this?
How can you tell?**

Pierre Bonnard, *The Breakfast Room*

**What are these three girls doing?
Where do you think they are?**

Jacob Lawrence, *The Migration of the Negro*

Do you think this boy wants to practice the piano? Where do you think he would like to be instead?

Henri Matisse, *Piano Lesson*

**These girls are swinging from a pole.
Does it seem dangerous?
What about the building behind them?**

Ben Shahn, *Liberation*

You can also make pictures of the city—
full of buildings, cars, and signs. Look at the
colors and lines. Can you hear any noise?

Jean Dubuffet, *Business Prospers*

Maybe she is dreaming of a quiet night and a gentle lion. What else can you imagine about this story?

Henri Rousseau, *The Sleeping Gypsy*

Do you have any stories to tell in pictures?

From A Young Painter

by Zheng Zhensun and Alice Low

Wang Yani was born in China in 1975. Like her father, Yani became interested in painting. Yani's father always encouraged her, even when her pictures were just scribbles.

When Yani was only three years old, she painted pictures of cats and monkeys. Her father was amazed that the pictures were so good. At the age of four, her paintings were shown in several cities in China. The Chinese people agreed that Yani was a wonderful painter.

Yani has painted more than ten thousand pictures since she was three. She often used monkeys or other animals instead of people in her paintings. Now that she is older, she paints the people and places of China.

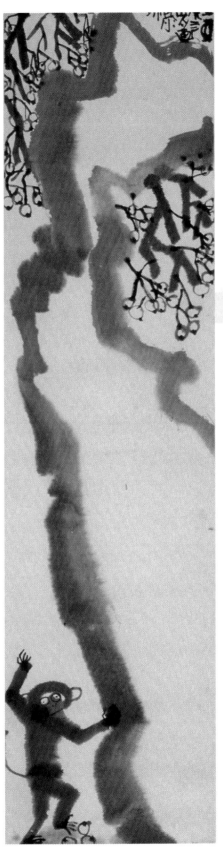

Many of Yani's paintings have stories that go with them. In *Is There a Moon on the Water?*, Yani says a baby monkey is taking a ride on its mother's back and looking for the moon in the water. In *Who Picked the Fruit?*, a little monkey is looking up at a tree hoping for fruit, but the fruit is gone.

Is There a Moon on the Water? Age 4

Who Picked the Fruit? Age 4

In *Going Home*, Yani explains that a monkey is so busy looking for fruit that he gets lost. Luckily, an ox comes along, and gives him a ride all the way home!

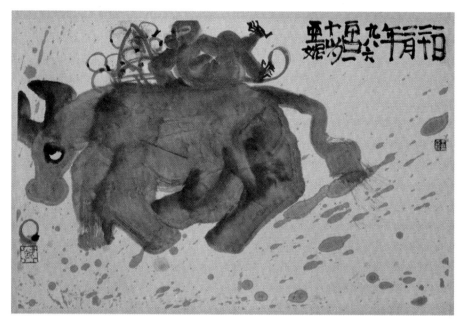

Going Home Age 10

Carrying the Sedan Chair Age 6

Yani's experiences of things she has seen and felt in real life are reflected in her monkey paintings, too. For example, Yani painted *Carrying the Sedan Chair* after she had seen brides in her town being carried to their new husbands' homes. This is an ancient Chinese custom.

Glossary

author
a person who writes a book or story
Laurie is the **author** of a story about her family.

buried
put in the earth or sea
The dog **buried** a bone in the garden.

charming
nice to be with
Our new neighbor is a **charming** lady.

comfortable
giving a nice feeling
The pillow was a **comfortable** place to rest his head.

considerate
kind, thoughtful of others' feelings
It is **considerate** to ask a new classmate to play with you.

cozy
comfortable and warm
The fire in the big fireplace made us feel **cozy** in our new house.

dangerous
not safe
It is **dangerous** to play with matches.

disaster
an event that causes much trouble or pain
The storm was a **disaster** that blew out windows in many homes.

erupting
breaking open suddenly
An **erupting** volcano threw steam and lava into the air.

fairy tales
stories about magical creatures and the things that happen to them

Cinderella and *Little Red Riding Hood* are my favorite **fairy tales**.

gentle
kind, not rough

When you pet a cat or dog, please be **gentle**.

gold
a yellow metal

The coins were made of **gold**.

grumpy
in a bad mood

Some people are **grumpy** early in the morning.

horrid
very bad, terrible

Someone who is mean to others is **horrid**.

gold

hungry
wanting food

The children felt very **hungry** at dinnertime.

ideas
thoughts

Mike has some good **ideas** about games we can play.

kind
nice, helpful to others

The doctor was **kind** to sick children and their families.

lava

hot, melted rock that comes out of a volcano

Hot **lava** is dripping down the sides of the volcano.

medium-sized

of a size between small and large

The **medium-sized** shirt fit better than the small one.

mystery

something that is not known or is secret

We solved the **mystery** of the lost money by finding the hole in the bag.

novel

a long story about make-believe people and the things they do

The **novel** is about a boy and his trip to the river.

pitch

to move suddenly from being flat to being crooked or at an angle

The earthquake made their floor shake and **pitch** to one side.

poem

a piece of writing with a special rhythm

"Twinkle, Twinkle, Little Star" is a **poem** many children love.

quiet

not noisy

When everyone is asleep, the house is very **quiet**.

lava

science fiction
a story that uses ideas from science to tell about things that happen but are not real

The **science fiction** story was about a spaceship from Mars that came to Earth.

solves
finds the answer to a problem or mystery

Earning this money **solves** the problem of how to pay for her present.

volcano

treasure

sweet
nice, easy to like

Tara is a **sweet** girl.

treasure
money, jewels, or other things of great value

There are pieces of gold, a crown, rings, and necklaces in the queen's **treasure**.

volcano
an opening in the ground from which come hot melted rocks and steam

That **volcano** looks like a mountain with a big hole in the top.

wicked
very, very bad

People who hurt others on purpose are **wicked**.

Authors and Illustrators

Miriam Cohen
pages 104-119

Miriam Cohen remembers all the funny things that happened when her children were in school. She uses some of those things to help make her stories seem so real and so funny. Cohen wrote another book about Jacob and his classmates, called *Second-Grade Friends, Again!* She has also written many books about other characters, including *No Good in Art* and *Best Friends*.

Larry Johnson pages 84-99

Larry Johnson uses his talent as an artist in many ways. He sometimes does sports cartoons for magazines and newspapers. He designs art for T-shirts. Besides *The Treasure Hunt* Johnson has illustrated other picture books, including *Knoxville, Tennessee* by Nikki Giovanni.

James Marshall pages 10-33

James Marshall always loved drawing and playing the viola. He was planning to be a musician until he hurt his hand. He couldn't play the viola, but he could still draw pictures. Marshall started illustrating books. Soon he was also writing funny stories about characters like Miss Nelson. He has also retold and illustrated *Goldilocks and the Three Bears* and *The Three Little Pigs*.

Jerry Tello pages 36-50

When Jerry Tello was a teenager, he was often asked to baby-sit for his younger brothers and sisters. He soon found that telling them funny stories was a good way to keep them happy. Now he travels all over the country telling stories in both English and Spanish. Two of Tello's stories that have been published as books are *Amalia and the Grasshopper* and *A New Batch of Tortillas*.

Acknowledgments

Grateful acknowledgment is made to the following sources for permission to reprint from previously published material. The publisher has made diligent efforts to trace the ownership of all copyrighted material in this volume and believes that all necessary permissions have been secured. If any errors or omissions have inadvertently been made, proper corrections will gladly be made in future editions.

Cover: Cover illustration copyright © 1990 by Tomie dePaola. Reprinted from LITTLE GRUNT AND THE BIG EGG by permission of Holiday House, Inc. All rights reserved.

Interior: "Red Riding Hood" from RED RIDING HOOD by James Marshall. Copyright © 1987 by James Marshall. Reprinted by permission of Dial Books for Young Readers, a division of Penguin Books USA Inc.

"And Still More Tales": Cover from RED RIDING HOOD by Beatrice Schenk de Regniers, illustrated by Edward Gorey. Illustration copyright © 1972 by Edward Gorey. Reprinted by permission of Atheneum Books for Young Readers, Simon & Schuster Children's Publishing Division. Cover and detail from the book cover from RUBY by Michael Emberley. Copyright © 1990 by Michael Emberley. Reprinted by permission of Little, Brown and Company. Cover from FLOSSIE & THE FOX by Patricia C. McKissack, pictures by Rachel Isadora. Pictures copyright © 1986 by Rachel Isadora. Used by permission of Dial Books for Young Readers, a division of Penguin Books USA Inc. Cover by Rachel Isadora from her THE PRINCESS AND THE FROG. Copyright © 1989 by Rachel Isadora. Reprinted by permission of Greenwillow Books, a division of William Morrow & Company, Inc. Cover from THE FROG PRINCE by Edith H. Tarcov, illustrated by James Marshall. Illustration copyright © 1974 by James Marshall. Reprinted by permission of Scholastic Inc. Cover from THE FROG PRINCE CONTINUED by Jon Scieszka, illustrated by Steve Johnson. Illustration copyright © 1991 by Steve Johnson. Used by permission of Viking Penguin, a division of Penguin Books USA Inc. Cover from CINDERELLA: THE UNTOLD STORY as told by Russell Shorto, illustrated by T. Lewis. Illustration copyright © 1990 by T. Lewis. Reprinted by permission of Carol Publishing Group. A Birch Lane Press Book. Cover and detail from the book cover from SIDNEY RELLA AND THE GLASS SNEAKER by Bernice Myers. Copyright © 1985 by Bernice Myers. This edition is reprinted by arrangement with Simon & Schuster Books for Young Readers, Simon and Schuster Children's Publishing Division. Cover from YEH-SHEN: A CINDERELLA STORY FROM CHINA by Ai-Ling Louie, illustrated by Ed Young. Illustration copyright © 1982 by Ed Young. Reprinted by permission of Philomel Books. Cover from JACK AND THE BEANSTALK, illustrated by Matt Faulkner. Illustration copyright © 1986 by Matt Faulkner. Reprinted by permission of Scholastic Inc. Cover from JACK AND THE BEANSTALK by Alan Garner, illustrated by Julek Heller. Illustration copyright © 1992 by Julek

Heller. Used with permission of Dell Books, a division of Bantam Doubleday Dell Publishing Group, Inc. Cover from JIM AND THE BEANSTALK by Raymond Briggs. Illustration copyright © 1970 by Raymond Briggs. Reprinted by permission of Coward-McCann, Inc. Cover from THE MOUSE BRIDE: A MAYAN FOLK TALE by Judith Dupré, illustrated by Fabricio Vanden Broeck. Illustration copyright © 1993 by Fabricio Vanden Broeck. Reprinted by permission of Alfred A. Knopf, Inc. Cover from MOUSE'S MARRIAGE by Anne Bower Ingram, illustrated by Junko Morimoto. Illustration copyright © 1985 by Junko Morimoto. Used by permission of Viking Penguin, a division of Penguin Books USA Inc. Cover and detail from the book cover from THE MOUSE BRIDE: A CHINESE FOLKTALE, retold by Monica Chang, illustrated by Lesley Liu. Copyright © 1992 by Yuan-Liou Publishing Co., Ltd. Reprinted by permission of the publisher.

ABUELO AND THE THREE BEARS by Jerry Tello, illustrated by Ana López Escrivá. Copyright © 1996 by Scholastic Inc.

Selection from "Who's Been Sleeping in My Porridge?" by Colin McNaughton and illustration of the "Backyard Players." Copyright © 1990 by Colin McNaughton. Published by Ideals Children's Books, an imprint of Hambleton-Hill Publishing, Inc., Nashville, TN. All rights reserved. Reprinted by permission of the publisher. Also by permission of the publisher Walker Books Limited. Cover from BIG BEAR'S TREASURY, VOL. 3. Cover illustration copyright © 1994 Helen Oxenbury. Used by permission of the publisher Candlewick Press.

"Little Grunt and the Big Egg" from LITTLE GRUNT AND THE BIG EGG by Tomie dePaola. Copyright © 1990 by Tomie dePaola. Reprinted by permission of Holiday House.

THE TREASURE HUNT by Angela Shelf Medearis, illustrated by Larry Johnson. Copyright © 1996 by Scholastic Inc.

"The Real Author" and cover from SECOND-GRADE FRIENDS by Miriam Cohen. Text copyright © 1993 by Miriam Cohen. Cover illustrated by Diane Palmisciano. Illustration copyright © 1993 by Scholastic Inc. Reprinted by permission.

Selection from WAKE ME IN SPRING by James Preller, illustrated by Jeffrey Scherer. Text copyright © 1994 by James Preller. Illustrations copyright © by Jeffrey Scherer. Published by Scholastic Inc. Reprinted by permission.

Selections and cover from STORIES by Philip Yenawine. Copyright © 1991 by Philip Yenawine. Reprinted by permission of Delacorte Press, a division of Bantam Doubleday Dell Publishing Group, Inc.

Selections and cover from A YOUNG PAINTER: THE LIFE AND PAINTINGS OF WANG YANI—CHINA'S EXTRAORDINARY YOUNG ARTIST by Zheng Zhensun and Alice Low. Text copyright © 1991 by New China Pictures Company. Cover illustration by Wang Yani, copyright © 1991 by Wang Shiqiang. Reprinted by permission of Scholastic Inc.

Cover from AUNT FLOSSIE'S HATS (AND CRAB CAKES LATER) by Elizabeth Fitzgerald Howard, illustrated by James Ransome. Illustration copyright © 1991 by James Ransome. Published by Clarion Books, a Houghton Mifflin Company imprint.

Cover from DEAR PETER RABBIT by Alma Flor Ada, illustrated by Leslie Tryon. Illustration copyright © 1994 by Leslie Tryon. Published by Atheneum Books for Young Readers, Simon & Schuster Children's Publishing Division.

Cover from THE STORIES JULIAN TELLS by Ann Cameron, illustrated by Ann Strugnell. Illustration copyright © 1981 by Ann Strugnell. Published by Random House, Inc.

Cover from THE TRUE STORY OF THE THREE LITTLE PIGS! by Jon Scieszka, illustrated by Lane Smith. Illustration copyright © 1989 by Lane Smith. Published by Viking Penguin, a division of Penguin Books USA Inc.

Photography and Illustration Credits

Selection Opener Photographs by David S. Waitz Photography/Alleycat Design, Inc.

Photos: pp. 2-3: © Suki Coughlin for Scholastic Inc. pp. 80-83 bl: © Suki Coughlin for Scholastic Inc. p. 100 cl: © Bob Daemmrich; cr: Courtesy of Angela Medearis. pp. 120-125: © Halley Ganges for Scholastic Inc. p. 126 c: © *In the North the Negro had better educational facilities,* panel from the series *The Great Migration* (1940-41) by Jacob Lawrence/The Museum of Modern Art, New York. Gift of Mrs. David Levy. p. 127 cl: © *The Sleeping Gypsy,* by Henri Rousseau/The Museum of Modern Art, New York. Gift of Mrs. Simon Guggenheim Fund; bl: © *The Breakfast Room,* by Pierre Bonnard/The Museum of Modern Art, New York. Given anonymously; cr: © *Piano Lesson,* by Henri Matisse/The Museum of Modern Art, New York. Mrs. Simon Guggenheim Fund; br: © *Liberation,* by Ben Shahn/The Museum of Modern Art, New York. James Thrall Soby Bequest. p. 128 c: © *The Breakfast Room,* by Pierre Bonnard/The Museum of Modern Art, New York. Given anonymously. p. 129 c: © *In the North the Negro had better educational facilities,* panel from the series *The Great Migration* (1940-41) by Jacob Lawrence/The Museum of Modern Art, New York. Gift of Mrs. David Levy. p. 130 c: © *Piano Lesson,* by Henri Matisse/The Museum of Modern Art, New York. Mrs. Simon Guggenheim Fund. p. 131 c: © *Liberation,* by Ben Shahn/The Museum of Modern Art, New York. James Thrall Soby Bequest. p. 132 c: © "Business Prospers," by Jean DuBuffet/The Museum of Modern Art, New York. Mrs. Simon Guggenheim Fund. p. 133 c: © *The Sleeping Gypsy,* by Henri Rousseau/The Museum of Modern Art, New York. Gift of Mrs. Simon Guggenheim Fund. p. 134 cl: © Glofa Enterprises; bc © Bie Bostrom for Scholastic Inc.; bl: © Bie Bostrom for Scholastic Inc. p. 135 cl: © *Is There a Moon on the Water?,* by Wang Yani/Glofa